*A book
is a present you can open
again and again.*

THIS BOOK BELONGS TO

_____

FROM

_____

Read Along Songs

This Old Man
CAME ROLLING HOME

Illustrated by Dennis Hockerman

World Book, Inc.
a Scott Fetzer company
Chicago London Sydney Toronto

Printed in the United States of America
ISBN 0-7166-1609-2
Library of Congress Catalog Card No. 91-65491

5 6 7 8 9 10 11 12 13 14 15 99 98 97 96 95 94

Cover design by Rosa Cabrera

This old man,

He played one,
He played knick-knack on my drum.
Knick-knack, paddy-whack,
Give a dog a bone,
This old man came rolling home.

This old man, he played two,
He played knick-knack on my shoe.
Knick-knack, paddy-whack,
Give a dog a bone,
This old man came rolling home.

This old man, he played three,
He played knick-knack on my knee.

Knick-knack, paddy-whack,
Give a dog a bone,
This old man came rolling home.

This old man, he played four,
He played knick-knack on my door.
Knick-knack, paddy-whack,
Give a dog a bone,
This old man came rolling home.

This old man, he played five,
He played knick-knack on my hive.

Knick-knack, paddy-whack,
Give a dog a bone,
This old man came rolling home.

This old man, he played six,
He played knick-knack with some sticks.
Knick-knack, paddy-whack,
Give a dog a bone,
This old man came rolling home.

This old man, he played seven,
He played knick-knack up to heaven.

Knick-knack, paddy-whack,
Give a dog a bone,
This old man came rolling home.

This old man, he played eight,
He played knick-knack on my gate.
Knick-knack, paddy-whack,
Give a dog a bone,
This old man came rolling home.

This old man, he played nine,
He played knick-knack on my vine.
Knick-knack, paddy-whack,
Give a dog a bone,
This old man came rolling home.

This old man, he played ten,
He played knick-knack once again.
Knick-knack, paddy-whack,
Give a dog a bone,
This old man came rolling home.

This old man,   he played one,   he played knick-knack

on   my   drum.   Knick - knack, pad - dy-whack,

give   a   dog   a   bone,   this   old   man   came   roll - ing home.

This old man, he played two,
He played knick-knack on my shoe.

This old man, he played three,
He played knick-knack on my knee.

This old man, he played four,
He played knick-knack on my door.

This old man, he played five,
He played knick-knack on my hive.

This old man, he played six,
He played knick-knack with some sticks.

This old man, he played seven,
He played knick-knack up to heaven.

This old man, he played eight,
He played knick-knack on my gate.

This old man, he played nine,
He played knick-knack on my vine.

This old man, he played ten,
He played knick-knack once again.

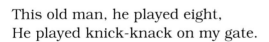

The End

To Parents

Children love words and music. *This Old Man Came Rolling Home* will give your child an opportunity for playful reading or singing, as well as a bridge into learning some important concepts. Here are a few easy and natural ways your child can express feelings and understandings about this song-poem. You know your child and can best judge which ideas he or she will enjoy most.

Add actions when you sing *This Old Man Came Rolling Home* with your child. For example, you may want to clap, slap your thighs, and snap your fingers when you sing "knick-knack, paddy-whack"; hold out an imaginary bone when you sing "give a dog a bone"; and rotate hand-over-hand when you sing "This old man came rolling home." Encourage your child to join in and even make up actions.

As you read or sing *This Old Man Came Rolling Home* with your child, pause before naming what the man played knick-knack on. Encourage your child to complete the phrase. Do so throughout the song as long as the activity holds your child's attention.

You and your child can enjoy counting along with this song. Each time you sing the name of a number, hold up that many fingers. For example, raise two fingers when you sing, "This old man, he played two." Your child will probably join in the action in no time.

Your child may enjoy making a drum to play while singing this song. Give your child a cylinder-shaped box or carton to paint or decorate with Contact Paper. The eraser-ends of pencils make good drumsticks. Invite your child to play the drum as you sing together.

In songs, children enjoy hearing their own names or the names of people they know. Sing *This Old Man Came Rolling Home* with your child's name. You can also change the character to a little boy or girl, a big brother, or even a brown dog. Encourage your child to draw a picture about one or more verses from the song you wrote.